BREAKTHROUGH

Crossrail's tunnelling story

Edited by Sarah Allen

Breakthrough. Crossrail's tunnelling story

This edition published in the United Kingdom in 2015 by
Crossrail Limited: 25 Canada Square,
Canary Wharf, London, E14 5LQ.

Text © Crossrail Limited 2015
Design & Layout © Crossrail Limited 2015

Map page 72-73 ©MAPS IN MINUTES™
Contains Ordnance Survey data ©Crown copyright and database right 2014

ISBN 978-0-9933433-0-8

Edited by Sarah Allen
Designed by Andrew Briffett
With contributions from Crossrail staff and its partners

Crossrail Limited is registered in England and Wales No. 4212657.
Registered Office: 25 Canada Square, Canary Wharf, London, E14 5LQ.

BREAKTHROUGH
Crossrail's tunnelling story

BREAKTHROUGH
Crossrail's tunnelling story

"Crossrail is an incredible feat of engineering that will help to improve the lives of working people in London and beyond. The project is a vital part of our long term plan to build a more resilient economy by helping businesses to grow, compete and create jobs right along the supply chain."

David Cameron MP, Prime Minister

"Crossrail will revolutionise east-west transit in the capital, making London an even more attractive place to visit and invest. This project is not just good for London; it's good for the whole of Britain, responsible for 55,000 jobs across the country and showing that the UK can deliver on major infrastructure projects."

Boris Johnson MP, Mayor of London

"The scale and complexity of Crossrail's tunnelling works is astounding and shows British engineering at its best. I look forward to the completion of the project which will play a vital role in driving forward our long term economic plan."

Patrick McLoughlin MP, Secretary of State for Transport

"Crossrail is vital to the future success of London and the UK. With London's population set to reach around ten million by 2030, we must continue to invest in improvements to London's transport network to create jobs and stimulate growth right across the UK, now and in the future."

Sir Peter Hendy CBE, London's Transport Commissioner (2006-2015)

  **MAYOR OF LONDON**

FOREWORD FROM TERRY MORGAN CBE CHAIRMAN, CROSSRAIL

Crossrail is more than a construction project. It is an investment in London and the UK and a very real expression of confidence in the ability and skills of the construction industry as a whole. The Crossrail project will deliver a new railway for London and the South East. It will reduce crowding, increase choice and reduce journey times across the capital.

The underground tunnels at the heart of this railway were designed on a scale not seen in this city before. We have had to innovate, to harness the latest technology and push established techniques to new limits to get the job done. Completing 42 kilometres of new tunnels under the city represents a huge milestone. While this significant feat of engineering is an achievement in itself, it is important to reflect on the way in which these new assets have been delivered.

The most important thing Crossrail has done lies in its wider impact on the industry, particularly in its contribution to improving and developing skills. Creating our Tunnelling and Underground Construction Academy, training the workforce to new industry standards and driving up the number of young people in the industry through the recruitment of over 400 apprentices, have been some of our proudest achievements.

This skilled workforce has been key to our success and will continue to be a benefit for many years to come. The works now move on to the finishing and fit out of new stations and the installation of systems that will turn these tunnels and wider infrastructure into an operating railway. After over three years of tunnelling under the city, this is the right time to recognise the contribution of every individual involved and celebrate a new asset built under London to support its future growth.

"Everyone involved can be justifiably proud of this achievement. It demonstrates the growing capability of the UK to deliver major infrastructure projects."

1 The challenge

LONDON IS GROWING

By 2030 the capital's population is set to reach ten million and its transport system must be ready to meet this demand. Crossrail is part of the UK's plan to maintain London's place as a world-class city.

The new railway will be a high frequency, high capacity service linking 40 stations over 100km, from Reading and Heathrow in the west to Shenfield and Abbey Wood in the east. It will reduce congestion by increasing central London's rail capacity by 10 per cent. It will create new routes into and through the city, giving 1.5 million additional people access to central London within 45 minutes. It will reduce journey times and deliver a world class, accessible experience for the travelling public.

To do all of this, the Crossrail project will build ten new stations, improve 30 more, upgrade existing rail infrastructure and construct some of London's largest and deepest underground rail tunnels.

Constructing these new tunnels would have been an incredible engineering challenge in itself. Achieving this underneath one of the world's greatest cities with the minimum of disruption as its inhabitants went about their daily lives in the streets above would require expertise, resourcefulness and resilience on a grand scale.

This is the story of that tunnelling journey...

"Crossrail is the biggest European civil engineering project of its time. The tunnelling work has been a massive undertaking, comparable to any of the great Victorian civil engineering enterprises that founded London's modern infrastructure."

Andrew Wolstenholme OBE
Chief Executive Officer, Crossrail

9

Crossrail's History

1974 — The London Rail Study is where Crossrail, as we know it today, was born

1989 — The Central London Rail Study (CLRS) included a Crossrail east-west route amongst proposals to manage population growth

1990 — Government gave the go-ahead to British Rail and London Underground to develop an east-west Crossrail scheme and safeguarded the route

1991 — A private Crossrail Bill was presented to Parliament but did not pass the select committee stage. The estimated project cost was £2 billion

1994 — The Railways Act was passed leading to the privatisation of British Rail. London Underground undertook a review of the central section of the Crossrail route

1999 — The Greater London Authority was established and the Mayor of London took over responsibility for parts of London's transport network. The Mayor's Transport Strategy including Crossrail went out to public consultation

2000 — The Department for the Environment, Transport and the Regions created the Strategic Rail Authority (SRA) and asked it to look at east–west travel across London.

2001 — A joint venture was created between SRA and Transport for London to take Crossrail forward. Cross London Rail Links Ltd. now known as Crossrail Ltd. was established.

2003 — The Crossrail scheme went out to public consultation

2004 — The Crossrail route was confirmed from Maidenhead and Heathrow in the west to Shenfield and Abbey Wood in the east, with new rail tunnels under central London linking existing railway east and west

2005 — The Crossrail Bill was submitted to Parliament. The estimated cost was £15 billion

2008 — The Crossrail Act was given Royal Assent. Transport for London (TfL) and the Department for Transport signed the Project Development Agreement. Crossrail Ltd became a wholly owned subsidiary of TfL

2009 — Construction on the railway began at Canary Wharf

2012 — Crossrail tunnelling began with the first tunnel boring machine, Phyllis, launched from the Royal Oak Portal

2014 — The Crossrail route was extended to Reading

2015 — Tunnelling ended with the final breakthrough of Victoria, the last of the eight tunnel boring machines, at Farringdon

2018 — Crossrail trains will run through central London tunnels

Going underground

Crossrail takes its place among a long history of tunnelling projects, undertaken to deliver vital infrastructure to service a vibrant capital city.

To deliver the increase in capacity demanded by the city's growth, it needed to be a mainline railway rather than a new London Underground line. This would mean creating a tunnel of 6.2 metres in diameter, almost twice the size of an average Tube tunnel. Delivering a new underground rail tunnel on this scale would be an enormous engineering challenge.

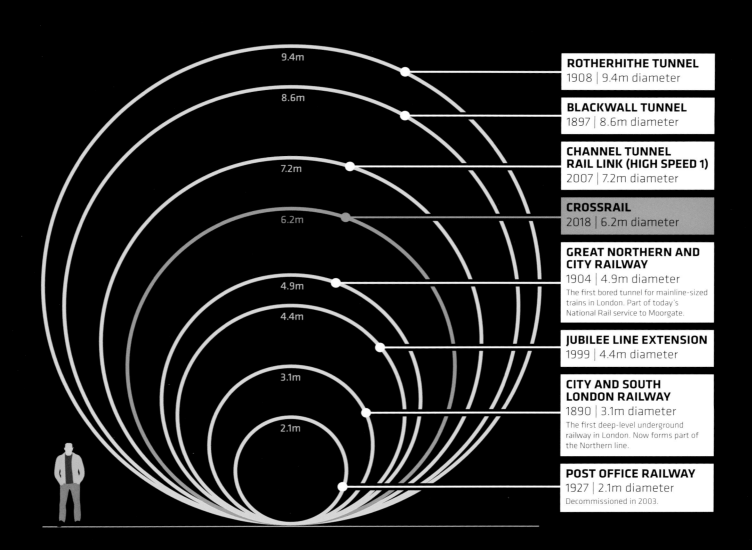

9.4m

8.6m

7.2m

6.2m

4.9m

4.4m

3.1m

2.1m

ROTHERHITHE TUNNEL
1908 | 9.4m diameter

BLACKWALL TUNNEL
1897 | 8.6m diameter

CHANNEL TUNNEL RAIL LINK (HIGH SPEED 1)
2007 | 7.2m diameter

CROSSRAIL
2018 | 6.2m diameter

GREAT NORTHERN AND CITY RAILWAY
1904 | 4.9m diameter
The first bored tunnel for mainline-sized trains in London. Part of today's National Rail service to Moorgate.

JUBILEE LINE EXTENSION
1999 | 4.4m diameter

CITY AND SOUTH LONDON RAILWAY
1890 | 3.1m diameter
The first deep-level underground railway in London. Now forms part of the Northern line.

POST OFFICE RAILWAY
1927 | 2.1m diameter
Decommissioned in 2003.

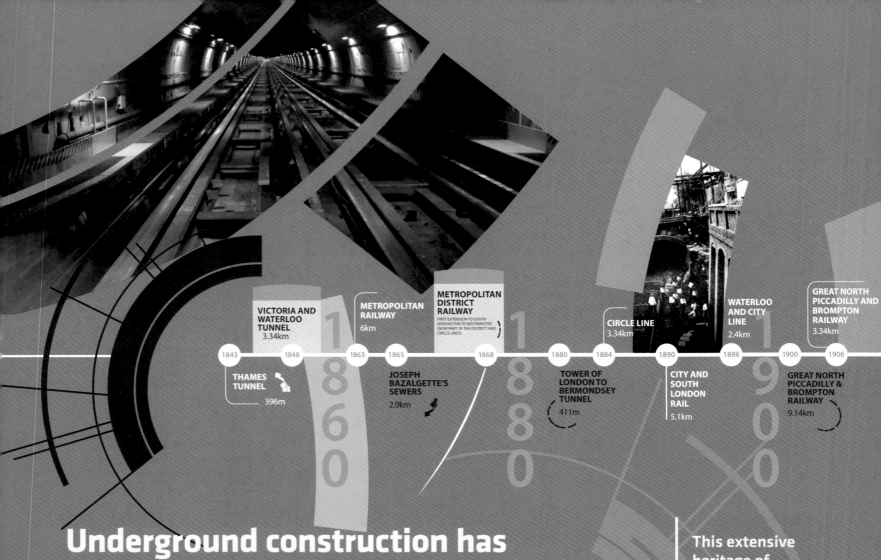

VICTORIA AND WATERLOO TUNNEL
3.34km

METROPOLITAN RAILWAY
6km

METROPOLITAN DISTRICT RAILWAY
FIRST EXTENSION TO SOUTH KENSINGTON TO WESTMINSTER (NOW PART OF THE DISTRICT AND CIRCLE LINES)

CIRCLE LINE
3.34km

WATERLOO AND CITY LINE
2.4km

GREAT NORTH PICCADILLY AND BROMPTON RAILWAY
3.34km

1843 — 1848 — 1863 — 1865 — 1868 — 1880 — 1884 — 1890 — 1898 — 1900 — 1906

THAMES TUNNEL
396m

JOSEPH BAZALGETTE'S SEWERS
2.9km

TOWER OF LONDON TO BERMONDSEY TUNNEL
411m

CITY AND SOUTH LONDON RAIL
5.1km

GREAT NORTH PICCADILLY & BROMPTON RAILWAY
9.14km

1860

1880

1900

Underground construction has been part of London's development for nearly 200 years and is an essential feature of its growing transport network.

This extensive heritage of tunnelling under the city has given London a complex subterranean landscape.

London's underground history

1908
ROTHERHITHE TUNNEL
1.5km

10.5km

POST OFFICE RAILWAY
1927

QUEENSWAY TUNNEL
3.2km
1934

DEEP LEVEL SHAFTS BUILT
3.7km
1942

1969
VICTORIA LINE
21km

1963
DARTFORD TUNNEL
14km

1969

JUBILEE LINE – FIRST PHASE
36.2km
1979

DOCKLANDS LIGHT RAILWAY
Extension under the Thames
1.6km
1991

JUBILEE LINE EXTENSION
11.3km
1999
1999

CHANNEL TUNNEL RAIL LINK
50km

2003

CROSSRAIL TUNNELS
42km
2018 COMPLETION DATE

2018

Planning the route

Expert tunnel designers had to plan how best to deliver the Crossrail route through a complex web of Victorian sewers, existing underground railway lines, utility pipes, services and building foundations. It was a complex and challenging task.

The solution for Crossrail's tunnels was to weave between existing structures, at times diving deeper than ever before. The majority of the tunnels would run 30 metres below ground, but reaching depths of up to 40 metres where necessary. This allowed the new route to avoid the extensive existing underground structures while enabling escalators and lifts to transfer passengers to and from ground level.

The best underground route connected the key central stations from Paddington to Canary Wharf and under docks and the River Thames in the east, with the portals that would integrate the new tunnel with existing railways.

The new path under London involved 42 kilometres of running tunnels for trains to run through, 14 kilometres of station tunnels and caverns, portals to link the new tunnels to existing overground parts of the rail line and shafts for ventilation.

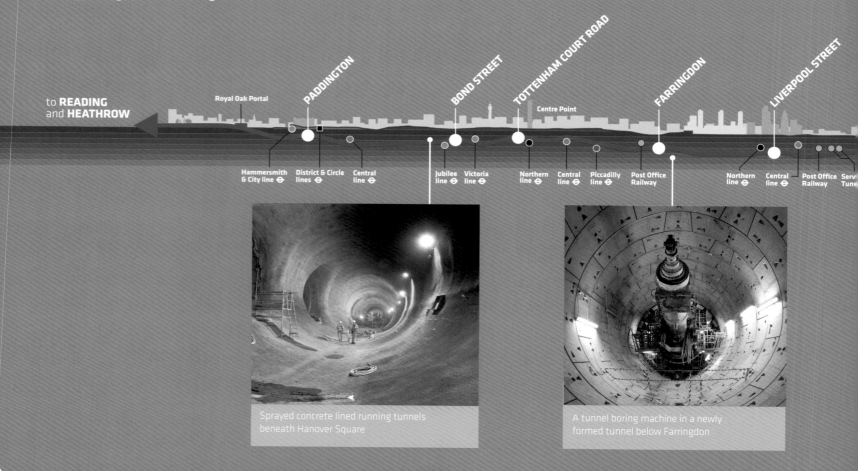

to **READING** and **HEATHROW**

Royal Oak Portal

PADDINGTON

BOND STREET

TOTTENHAM COURT ROAD

Centre Point

FARRINGDON

LIVERPOOL STREET

Hammersmith & City line

District & Circle lines

Central line

Jubilee line

Victoria line

Northern line

Central line

Piccadilly line

Post Office Railway

Northern line

Central line

Post Office Railway

Serv Tunn

Sprayed concrete lined running tunnels beneath Hanover Square

A tunnel boring machine in a newly formed tunnel below Farringdon

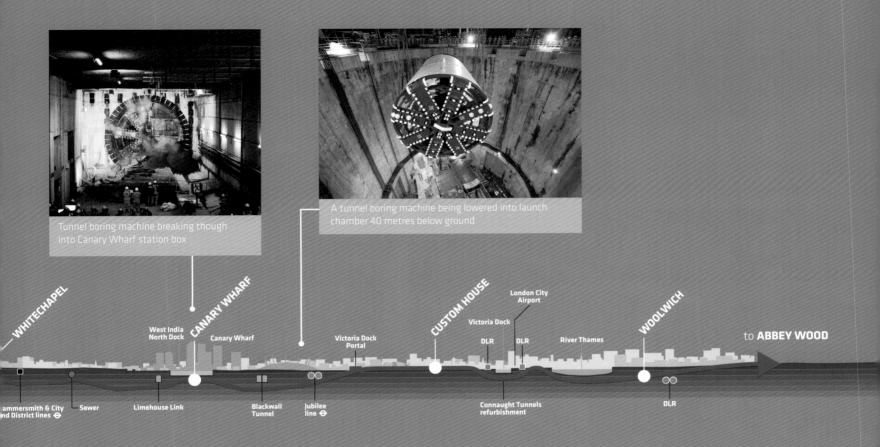

Tunnel boring machine breaking though into Canary Wharf station box

A tunnel boring machine being lowered into launch chamber 40 metres below ground

WHITECHAPEL

CANARY WHARF

CUSTOM HOUSE

WOOLWICH

London City Airport

Victoria Dock

West India North Dock

Canary Wharf

Victoria Dock Portal

DLR

DLR

River Thames

to **ABBEY WOOD**

ammersmith & City nd District lines

Sewer

Limehouse Link

Blackwall Tunnel

Jubilee line

Connaught Tunnels refurbishment

DLR

Crossrail's deep, large-scale route under London comprised three distinct underground spaces:

- **RUNNING TUNNELS**
- **STATION TUNNELS & CAVERNS**
- **CONNAUGHT TUNNEL**

If the Crossrail tunnels had been built by a single machine, it could have taken up to 15 years to deliver

RUNNING TUNNELS

At the heart of the Crossrail route are 42 kilometres of new tunnels that stretch under central London, connecting existing railways to the west out of Paddington and to the east out of Liverpool Street.

The pair of tunnels, one each for eastbound and westbound services, stretch from a portal at Royal Oak in west London. They link up Crossrail's central stations before splitting into two routes in east London. In the north east the tunnels continue to a portal at Pudding Mill Lane. In the south east the tunnels run to Victoria Dock portal and then under the Thames to Woolwich.

The precise route of the tunnels was chosen after extensive surveys were undertaken to consider the potential impact on many thousands of buildings above the route, including hundreds of listed buildings. The route had to weave around foundations, existing Tube lines, sewers, utilities and other underground infrastructure. At Tottenham Court Road, one of London's most congested underground locations, the route had to be built within a metre of an operational Tube platform.

Building the running tunnels was divided into five tunnel drives, with each drive comprising two tunnel boring machines and their specialist crews of up to 20 workers. The tunnel drives would generate 3.4 million tonnes of spoil and require over 200,000 concrete segments to line the tunnel walls.

Twin-bore tunnelling in this way presented a number of advantages, including:

• Reducing the time required to construct the tunnels

• Reducing the number of shafts needed to lower machinery and gain access to the tunnels, minimising disruption at ground level

• Reducing maintenance issues created by longer tunnel drives whilst running the machines as closely as possible to their working lifespan

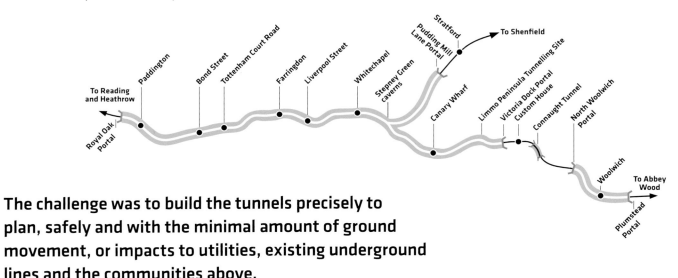

The challenge was to build the tunnels precisely to plan, safely and with the minimal amount of ground movement, or impacts to utilities, existing underground lines and the communities above.

Earth matters

Before tunnelling could begin, detailed investigation of the ground had to be undertaken. Ground investigations were performed by taking core samples from various locations along the route.

A core sample is taken by drilling a cylindrical section of earth to determine the type of earth and the number of geological strata at a given location. Over 1,000 core samples were taken before tunnelling began.

The core samples confirmed the type of ground Crossrail would be tunnelling through. The various geological strata included:

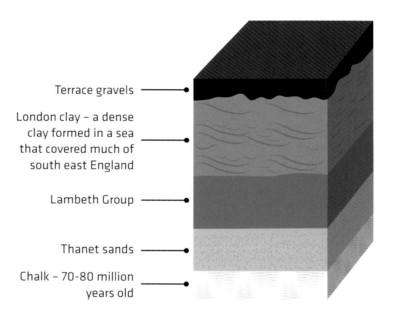

Terrace gravels

London clay – a dense clay formed in a sea that covered much of south east England

Lambeth Group

Thanet sands

Chalk – 70-80 million years old

The samples showed how millions of years of geological activity have shaped the ground on which London sits.

This detailed testing determined the machines to be used and the mitigations to be undertaken to control settlement of the buildings and infrastructure above.

STATION TUNNELS & CAVERNS

Crossrail would need to create some of the largest underground spaces ever built in London. The spaces were required to create passenger walkways, station platforms, portals and underground caverns for train crossover points and they needed to be delivered using a different technique to the running tunnels.

Building these non-uniform structures required an established mining method, called sprayed concrete lining. This technique had been used successfully on many rail and other infrastructure projects, including the Jubilee line Extension. The construction of Crossrail required 14 kilometres of varied tunnels and large cavernous spaces in addition to the 42 kilometres of running tunnels. To deliver on this scale, the process would need refining further.

CONNAUGHT TUNNEL

Connaught Tunnel represented the third type of underground space on the route. Built under the Royal Docks in east London, the tunnel was previously part of the North London Railway. Disused since 2006, the 550 metre structure would need to be enlarged to accommodate Crossrail trains and overhead power supply. The works would be delivered in a functioning dock holding 13 million litres of water.

"My job was to give the project heart, to get on and deliver and give everyone involved the confidence to do it. Whatever role we undertook, wherever we worked, whoever we worked for, we were all part of the same project, sharing common values and working towards the same goal"

**Andrew Wolstenholme
Chief Executive Officer
Crossrail**

Building the team

Crossrail required the mobilisation of the country's best design consultants, engineers, project managers, contractors and suppliers to build the tunnels safely, on time and within the funding available.

The team had to be large, highly skilled and responsive to the changing requirements of the programme. It needed to be focused and collaborative, working with one culture despite the huge number of separate organisations involved. Anyone working on Crossrail from pit boss to finance director felt they were part of the same team. Values were key and summed up by the phrase 'together we're moving London forward'. Safety was always the number one value; every member of the team was charged with taking responsibility, aiming for zero harm across the project. Other values included inspiration and collaboration, encouraging the teams to tackle surprises head on, to be inventive and to be curious enough to look over the horizon and anticipate the unexpected.

Creating confidence in the whole team from the management organisation to each individual driving a tunnel boring machine was vital to deliver a job at such a large scale. Expert panels were used to assess proposals, designs and working practices in order to challenge and verify the way works were being undertaken. This collaboration and the effective relationships with Crossrail's many partners ensured the successful delivery of a complex task.

The team also needed momentum; London needed a new railway by 2018 and the team had to deliver the tunnels by 2015 to keep the project on plan. Vital to the project's progress was to ensure the tunnelling teams understood that they were the first step in a scheme to build a whole railway.

**2,827 people
previously not
in work gained
employment in
tunnelling operations**

Developing the workforce

A major challenge of Crossrail was to mobilise the large, skilled workforce required to deliver the tunnelling job. Early on, it became apparent that the existing UK industry did not have enough people with the specialist experience and skills necessary to support the project. To directly address the shortage Crossrail would look to inspire new people to work in the industry and provide specialist training as well as gathering the best skills and experience already available in underground construction.

Crossrail established the Tunnelling and Underground Construction Academy (TUCA) in 2011 to directly address the shortage of people with the necessary skills.

TUCA is a purpose-built training facility that supports the skills required to work in tunnel excavation, underground construction and infrastructure. The only soft-ground tunnelling training facility in Europe, it offers courses on sprayed concrete lining, plant and tunnel operations and safety. Crossrail worked with industry, professional bodies and other organisations to ensure that the facilities and training at TUCA were aligned with the wider needs of the industry. By doing so, Crossrail contributed to the development of new qualifications and health and safety standards.

Increasing new entrants into the world of construction would also be vital to Crossrail's tunnelling success. Crossrail proactively employed apprentices and engineering graduates throughout the programme, setting a target of employing 400 apprentices which was surpassed by the end of 2014. One hundred and sixty five of them were directly involved in delivering and supporting tunnelling operations.

The volume of underground construction work taking place in the UK over the next decade is unprecedented. The Thames Tideway tunnel, London Underground work and electricity cable tunnel projects all require significant numbers of skilled people. Longer term, the same skills may be required for Crossrail 2 and High Speed 2. TUCA and the skilled Crossrail workforce will continue to contribute to the industry, supporting the delivery of these vital infrastructure projects.

Over 10,000 training sessions were delivered by the Tunnelling & Underground Construction Academy

Breaking through

BUILDING NEW TUNNELS BENEATH LONDON

Building the Crossrail tunnels represented an engineering challenge on an unprecedented scale.

As ambitious as the major infrastructure projects of the Victorian age, the job demanded the work of thousands of people, using some of the world's most technologically advanced machines and the refinement of construction techniques that have been evolving for nearly two hundred years.

The tunnelling journey began in 2012...

"It is impossible to overstate the scale of this engineering challenge and how impressive the works have been on sites all over and under London."

Simon Wright OBE
Programme Director, Crossrail

TUNNEL BORING MACHINES

Eight specially built tunnel boring machines were manufactured to construct the new rail tunnels under London. The machines were built and tested in Germany and shipped over in parts to the UK. They arrived in 2012 to commence the work of carving out the Crossrail tunnels beneath the heart of the capital.

Weighing 1,000 tonnes and measuring 148 metres long, they operated as underground factories; tunnelling, removing excavated material and creating a sealed concrete tunnel.

Six were Earth Pressure Balance machines that forged through the clay, sand and gravel in the western and central parts of the route. Two were Mix Shield Slurry machines that drove through the wet chalk and flint beneath the River Thames.

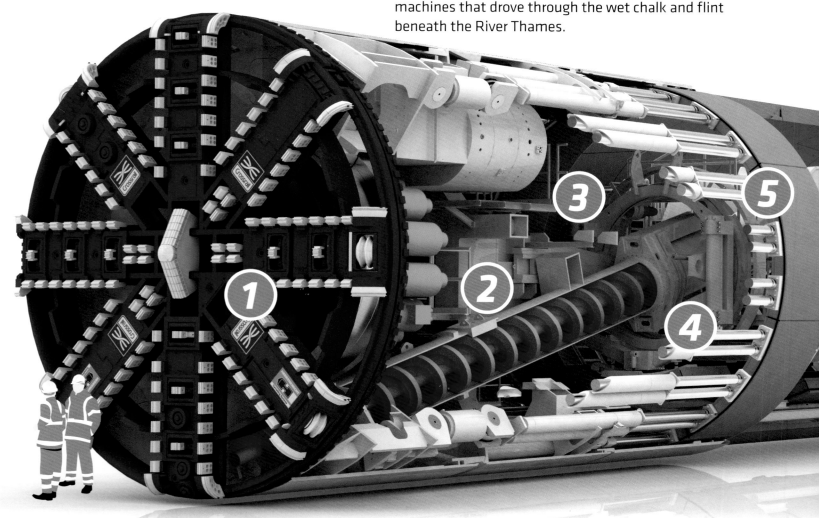

THE EARTH PRESSURE BALANCE
TUNNEL BORING MACHINE

1 The rotating cutter head loosens the earth.

2 A screw conveyor moves the earth away from the cutter head.

3 A rotating arm installs concrete segments to form a ring.

4 Hydraulic rams brace themselves against the ring to push the machine forward.

5 Each ring is made up of eight segments and weighs 22 tonnes.

6 Pre-cast concrete segments are delivered to the feeder. They differ in shape to enable the tunnel to curve.

7 A belt conveyor system removes the earth from the machine.

TUNNEL BORING MACHINE FACTS

Length: 148 metres

Weight: 1,000 tonnes

Cost: £10 million

Average speed: 100 metres per week, working 24 hours per day

Crew: Up to 20 people operate the machine per shift

How the tunnel boring machines work

The Earth Pressure Balance machines work in two stages.

Firstly, the cutterhead rotates to excavate 1.6 metres of earth while the machine pushes against the concrete lining segments it has previously laid. The machine balances the pressure inside the cutterhead with that in front of it, to maintain the stability of the ground. The waste is removed by the conveyor belt while the excavation is underway and the shape of the tunnel walls is monitored throughout.

The machine then pauses its forward movement, while concrete segments are selected and installed to create a tunnel ring. Segments are chosen to best correspond to the subtle changes in tunnel shape and put into place using a vacuum control. Segments are positioned with millimetre precision and held in place with rams before being finally bolted into place. A wedge shaped keystone is put in as the final piece to complete the ring.

The hydraulic rams are extended again to secure the segments into position and the machine pushes off from the completed section, to excavate the next short segment of tunnel.

Under the river.

For the drives under the River Thames slurry machines were required to tunnel through chalk and flint beneath the river. These machines support the tunnel face and counterbalance groundwater pressure with slurry pressure to prevent the inward flow of groundwater.

Slurry machines have a sealed, pressurised, air-locked chamber behind the cutterhead. The excavated material is mixed with bentonite (a mixture of clay and water) to form a liquid, which is removed through an outlet pipe instead of through a dry conveyor belt.

Each tunnel boring machine weighs the same as three fully-laden jumbo jets

Concrete segment

Bolt

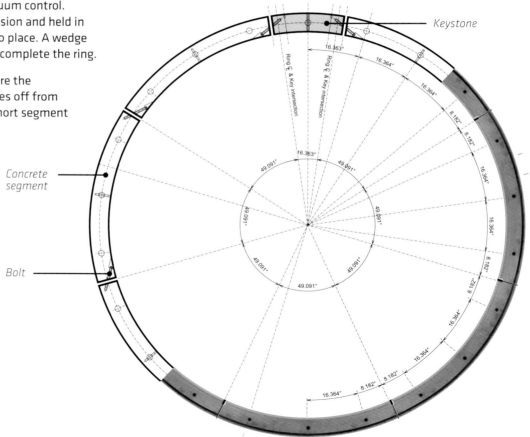

Keystone

The average mole tunnels at 800 metres an hour, many times faster than a tunnel boring machine which travels at 0.6 metres an hour

The force of a tunnel boring machine in operation is as strong as that needed to lift 2,900 London taxis!

Concrete segments

Over 200,000 concrete segments were required to line the 42 kilometres of running tunnels. Seven segments and a keystone were used to make up every tunnel ring, locked together to build a concrete tube reinforced with steel fibres, built to last for hundreds of years.

Each segment weighs 3,000 kilogrammes
Each keystone weighs 1,000 kilogrammes

Three factories manufactured the pre-cast concrete segments and keystones:

Crossrail's western tunnels
Factory in Old Oak Common, west London
Produced 75,000 tunnel segments
Employed 60 people (at its peak)

Crossrail's eastern tunnels
Factory in Chatham, Kent
Produced 110,000 tunnel segments
Employed 120 people (at its peak)

Crossrail's Thames Tunnel
Factory in Mulligar, Ireland
Produced 25,000 tunnel segments

"Crossrail is a fantastic project for Britain and a fantastic thing to do because of the value it brings to the economy and to employment locally."

**David Allen,
Finance Director, Crossrail**

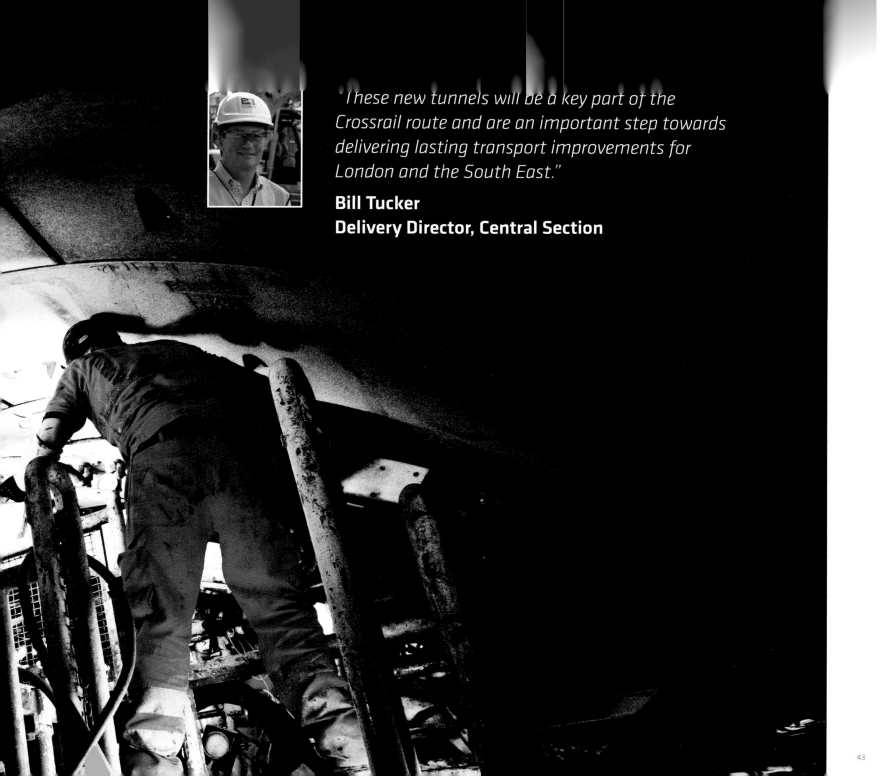

"These new tunnels will be a key part of the Crossrail route and are an important step towards delivering lasting transport improvements for London and the South East."

Bill Tucker
Delivery Director, Central Section

Naming the machines

Following mining tradition, Crossrail's tunnel boring machines were given women's names. A public competition was used to choose eight names of inspiring women:

Ada and Phyllis

Ada Lovelace was the world's first computer programmer. Phyllis Pearsall created the London A-Z.

Victoria and Elizabeth

Queen Victoria was monarch in the first age of great railway engineering projects.
Queen Elizabeth acceded to the throne at the advent of this great age of railway engineering projects.

Sophia and Mary

Sophia Brunel was the wife of Marc Isambard Brunel who built the first tunnel under the Thames.
Mary Brunel was the wife of the famous railway engineer Isambard Kingdom Brunel.

Jessica and Ellie

Jessica Ennis CBE was a 2012 Olympic gold medal winning track and field athlete.
Ellie Simmonds OBE was a 2012 Paralympic gold medal winning swimmer.

Saint Barbara

Saint Barbara is renowned for being the patron saint of construction workers, miners and tunnellers all over the world.

A painted statue of Saint Barbara watched over tunnel entrances during the mining works.

The construction railway

Keeping the machines supplied with materials was critical to maintaining production and was done via a temporary construction railway, laid behind the machines to move people and materials to and from the cutterhead. The trains and rolling stock were relatively small but carried heavy loads on narrow track, directly bolted to the tunnel floor.

Noise and vibration was minimised through the type of track used and good maintenance. Additional noise reduction measures were instigated at sensitive locations such as theatres, concert halls and recording studios.

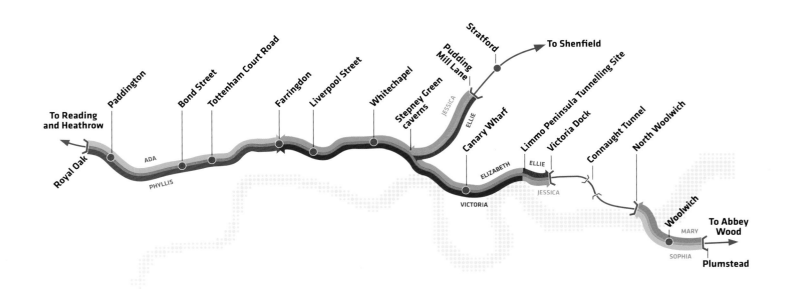

Monitoring ground movement

Any tunnelling carries a risk of ground movement at the surface and potential impacts to the buildings above. To minimise movement, tunnel boring machine crews maintained tight control of the pressure at the face of the machines, precisely correlating the rate of advance with the weight and volume of excavated material.

To monitor movement, consistent real-time data collection was essential to ensure structures were stable and buildings were unaffected by excavations below. Over 75,000 sensors were used to monitor the effect of tunnelling:

- Robotic theodolites compiled data from targeted prisms attached to buildings along the route

- Hydraulic levelling cells were used to detect small changes in water level

- Hand-held theodolites were used for manual monitoring at the surface

- Additional theodolites picked up data from prisms attached to the interior excavated walls of new tunnels

- Extensometers were installed to measure movement below ground

This wealth of data created a comprehensive picture of the impact of works and ensured the team could respond where necessary to protect the buildings above ground from damage. Overall settlement at the surface was well within the predictions and damage to buildings was actively managed throughout.

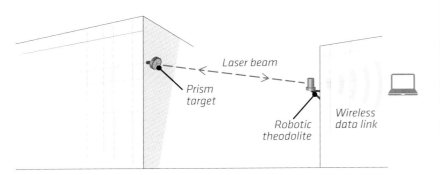

Laser beam

Prism target

Robotic theodolite

Wireless data link

CASE STUDY

LINDSEY STREET

In some locations, existing historic structures were particularly vulnerable to the effects of ground movement, however minimal. Lindsey Street in Farringdon was built on a bridge over a Victorian railway. To strengthen and stabilise the street, a slab was laid between the arches and steel lintel beams were installed with adjustable jacks that could be utilised to maintain street level stability during the tunnelling works beneath.

These underpinning works and mitigation techniques were completed prior to the excavations and protected the street and all its buildings for the duration of works.

Phyllis starts Crossrail's tunnelling journey

Crossrail tunnelling began with Phyllis at Royal Oak Portal in spring 2012 following an official ceremony with Boris Johnson, the Mayor of London, and the then Transport Secretary Justine Greening MP.

Travelling east towards Farringdon, Phyllis covered 6.4 kilometres underground via Paddington, Bond Street and Tottenham Court Road.

After careful navigation beneath London Underground's Hammersmith & City line, the Great Western Main Line and historical landmarks, Phyllis arrived at Farringdon in October 2013 completing her 17 month journey.

Following this breakthrough, Crossrail marked the completion of the first section of tunnel. To celebrate this significant milestone, a time capsule was created using a small drum from the tunnel boring machine, buried with Phyllis' cutterhead. Inside the capsule is the London A to Z, London transport collectables and items suggested by workers and community members.

The remainder of Phyllis was dismantled and removed from the tunnel via a shaft at Fisher Street.

Elizabeth and Victoria launched from the east

The tunnelling from Limmo Peninsula in east London to Farringdon was the longest tunnelling drive of the project. Elizabeth set off first in November 2012 and Victoria started a month later, building the tunnels from the east.

Launching a tunnel boring machine is a precise operation that requires meticulous planning. At Limmo, a 15 metre starter tunnel was built for each machine using sprayed concrete lining. A soft concrete headwall was constructed at the end of the tunnel in order to safely embed the cutterhead into the ground.

The size of the shaft at Limmo meant the machines had to be lowered in sections. The machines were lowered 35 metres into the shaft, onto rails known as a launch cradle. A large steel frame was constructed behind them to resist the pressure of the boring machines' backward thrust and allow them to launch forward. Once they had been pushed through the headwall, the rear sections were attached and they set off on their journeys underground.

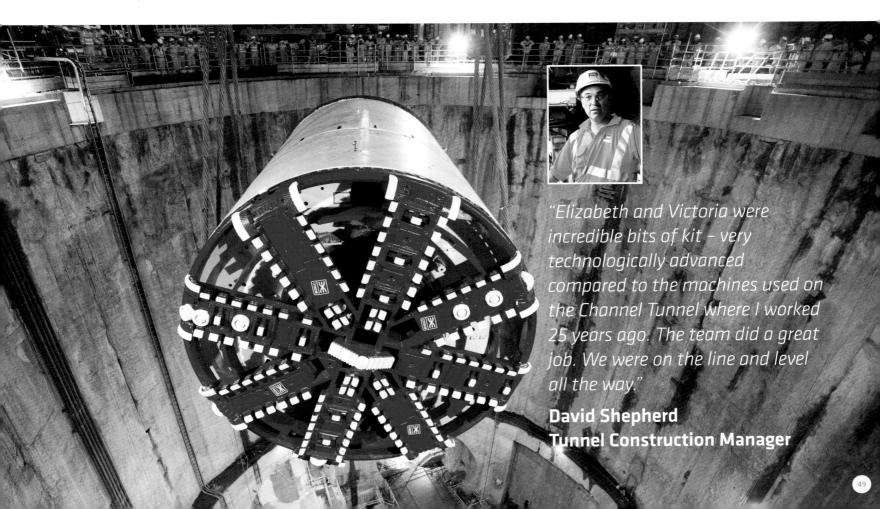

"Elizabeth and Victoria were incredible bits of kit – very technologically advanced compared to the machines used on the Channel Tunnel where I worked 25 years ago. The team did a great job. We were on the line and level all the way."

David Shepherd
Tunnel Construction Manager

49

Jessica and Ellie were used to construct the 2.7 kilometres of tunnels from Pudding Mill Lane portal to Stepney Green. On completion of the drives, the machines were dismantled and transported by road to Limmo Peninsula, where they were re-launched to drive through the tunnels from Limmo to Victoria Dock Portal.

They were the only machines on the project to undertake two separate tunnel drives.

Tunnel boring machine
Ellie travelled
a record 72 metres
on a single day

"There is a temptation on reaching a milestone on a project to look immediately towards the next challenge, and not to stop and celebrate the achievements which soon become forgotten. The day that Ada safely passed Tottenham Court Road station it was worth stopping to reflect on that achievement and how impressive the completion of these drives were."

Andy Alder
Project Manager, Western Tunnels

Ada squeezes through the eye of the needle

Ada's immense journey was much more challenging than that of her sister machine, Phyllis, due to the complexity of the underground landscape she was navigating.

Early in her journey Ada passed directly beneath the abutment of Lord Hill's Bridge. With a four metre clearance, there was little room for error for this giant machine. With careful management the machine passed the bridge with no impact to the structure. However, her greatest challenge was yet to come.

In building the route from Paddington to Farringdon, Ada had to navigate London Underground station structures at Tottenham Court Road and Goslett Yard. Ada came within 90 centimetres of live Northern line platforms and within 60 centimetres of passenger escalators. Squeezing the vast machine through such a narrow space without impacting structures or alarming passengers on live services was a significant challenge. While the low hum of the cutterhead could at times be heard in the Northern line station, the machine passed through keeping precisely to her course, with no impact on her surroundings.

Ada excavated over 6.8 kilometres of tunnel, and installed over 4,500 rings to build her part of the route.

The tunnel boring machine passed within 60 centimetres of passengers on escalators in London Underground's Tottenham Court Road station

Sophia and Mary build below the Thames

To deliver Crossrail services to Abbey Wood, new tunnels had to be built beneath the River Thames. Portals at Plumstead and North Woolwich were built prior to Sophia and Mary, Crossrail's two slurry machines, arriving to commence tunnelling in 2013.

The tunnels under the Thames represented a number of challenges.

Only one machine could drive at any time on this route, due to the constraints of the slurry processing factory, power and water, but the tunnels were completed in just 16 months.

A vital substation was located 4.5 metres above Sophia's route out of Plumstead, powering the North Kent Rail Line. A targeted injection of a liquid sand and cement mixture was used to raise the substation by three millimetres and create a cushion, while the machines passed by below. On the other side of the river, Sophia had to pass over existing DLR tunnels at Woolwich, coming within two metres of the live railway. Careful coordination and monitoring of the works meant the tunnel was delivered safely.

The slurry machines produce liquid waste, which required processing in a temporary factory on site at Plumstead. The factory separated cakes of excavated earth for recycling and the bentonite for reuse in the machines. The slurry treatment plant would usually use a substantial volume of drinking water. The local team reduced this requirement by using surplus groundwater for processes such as bentonite mixing, slurry dilution and grout mixing, saving over two million litres of potable water a week.

Tunnelling beneath the river was completed in May 2014. Sophia and Mary excavated around 500,000 tonnes of chalk and flint and installed 3,400 rings. The completed tunnels under the Thames are each 2.7 kilometres long and run 15 metres below the existing riverbed.

"Crossrail's construction has moved ahead at a significant pace. The tunnelling machines have been hard at work for the last three years building up to 100 metres of new tunnel every day."

Andy Mitchell CBE
Programme Director (2009-2014)

SPRAYED CONCRETE LINING

The first sight of Crossrail's underground public spaces may be a surprise to passengers. While the large scale of the Jubilee line Extension station platforms is familiar, the angular nature of access passages and stairwells are an established feature of London's underground stations. Crossrail's underground spaces will be curved and will offer more space for passengers, thanks to developments in sprayed concrete lining.

Fourteen kilometres of central London station platforms, escalator barrels, walking routes, shafts and underground caverns have been built using sprayed concrete lining. Chosen for its ability to adapt to variations in tunnel sizes and shapes, this technique has evolved over many years and has been used successfully on other underground rail projects. The scale of underground spaces required by the Crossrail project meant the process needed to be used on an even grander scale.

New materials have allowed the development of concrete that has early, controllable strength. This meant sprayed concrete lining could move on from its function as a temporary lining on projects such as the Jubilee line Extension, to deliver immediate support and permanently stable ground. This refined concrete, along with improvements in analysis of loading patterns, gave Crossrail the ability to excavate huge, cavernous spaces.

The sprayed concrete lining technique was used at many locations on Crossrail, including Stepney Green, Liverpool Street, Whitechapel, Tottenham Court Road, Bond Street, Limmo Peninsula, Fisher Street and Farringdon.

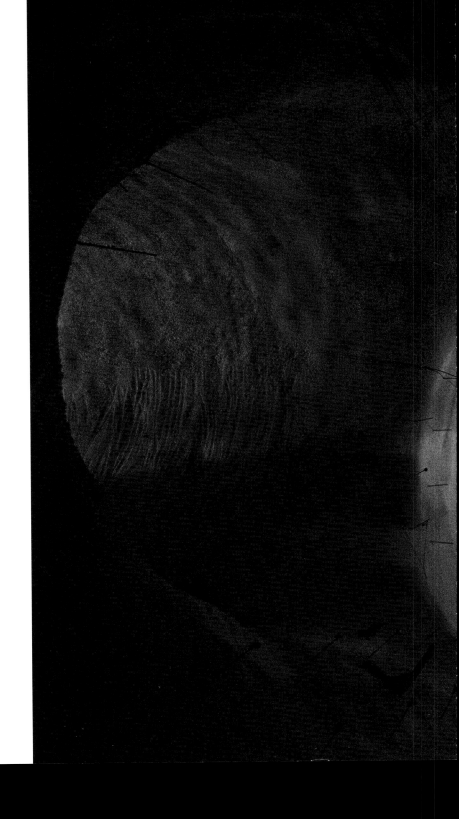

Refining the technique

To achieve large open face excavations in this new way, it was essential to tightly control the sprayed concrete lining process:

- A space, typically one metre in depth, is excavated

- The area is sprayed with a primary lining, using a robotic spraying machine operated by a skilled technician from outside an exclusion zone

- A waterproof lining is then applied in a thin layer

- A secondary lining of shotcrete (concrete reinforced with steel fibres) is sprayed to form the complete permanent tunnel lining

When complete, the sprayed concrete lining is approximately 60 centimetres thick and built to last for at least 120 years.

Advantages:

This technique demands the excavation of small areas at a time, which can help reduce ground movement. It allows the building of variable sizes, from small to very large cavernous spaces that are not achievable using tunnel boring machines.

It can be used to create a great variety of underground shapes, making it more flexible than other methods.

Challenges:

When used to create complex arrangements of tunnels in station environments, each tunnel generates movement individually. While each movement might be small, the cumulative effect can be substantial meaning a greater need for compensation measures.

The technique involves working in expansive, open areas where there is moving plant equipment, a complexity of tunnels and potential for ground movement, so the focus on safe ways of working must always be paramount.

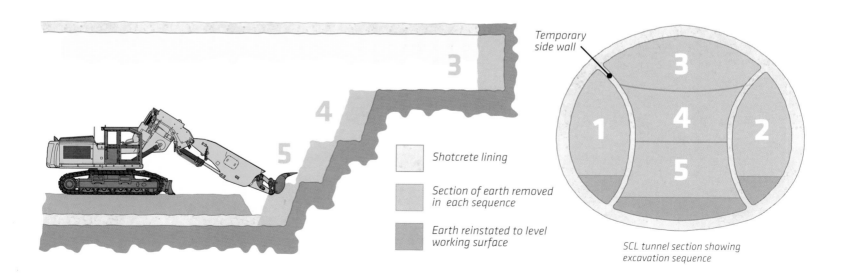

Temporary side wall

Shotcrete lining

Section of earth removed in each sequence

Earth reinstated to level working surface

SCL tunnel section showing excavation sequence

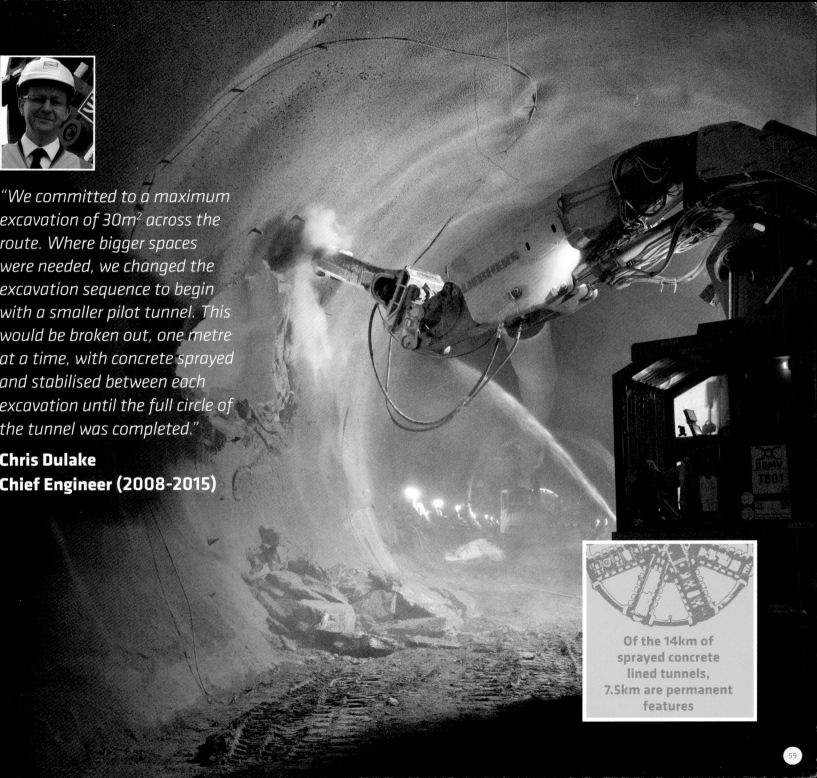

"We committed to a maximum excavation of 30m² across the route. Where bigger spaces were needed, we changed the excavation sequence to begin with a smaller pilot tunnel. This would be broken out, one metre at a time, with concrete sprayed and stabilised between each excavation until the full circle of the tunnel was completed."

Chris Dulake
Chief Engineer (2008-2015)

Of the 14km of sprayed concrete lined tunnels, 7.5km are permanent features

75km of grout pipes were utilised under London to protect buildings from ground movement

Stabilising the ground

While straight running tunnels present a simple pattern of ground movement, areas of shallow excavation or multiple tunnels posed a greater challenge. Station tunnels, platform tunnels, cross passages and escalator barrels often had to coexist in small areas; the cumulative ground movement effect could have been significant.

To help prevent any adverse impact to buildings on the surface and utilities around some construction sites, the ground was treated to compensate for any movement. Across central London a technique known as compensation grouting was used to stabilise the ground.

Engineers created a number of vertical shafts several metres deep. From the shaft walls, small horizontal pipes were installed into the earth radiating from the shaft. A cement-like substance known as grout was injected into the pipes, reaching deep into the ground. This process lifted the ground in specific locations and helped to reduce any differential settlement that may have occurred at the surface. When any ground movement has permanently settled, the shaft will be backfilled and the ground reinstated.

Compensation grouting was used at Bond Street, Tottenham Court Road, Farringdon, Liverpool Street and Whitechapel.

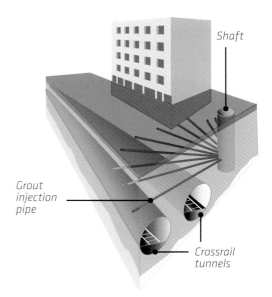

Shaft

Grout injection pipe

Crossrail tunnels

SWANLEA SCHOOL, WHITECHAPEL

In certain cases, buildings had to be completely isolated from the potential effects of tunnelling. Swanlea School sat directly above the Whitechapel tunnel drive. Ensuring there was no ground movement and that the school could continue to remain open to its pupils was essential. Underpinning works took place on the school foundations to jack up the structure in advance of the tunnel boring machines' drive below.

The works were successful; the children were able to carry on with their studies regardless of what was going on beneath their feet.

Groundwater

Excessive water in the ground can cause problems during tunnelling if left unchecked. High water pressures could create a risk of inundation of water and soil during tunnelling.

The solution was to drain away the excess water before tunnelling could begin, a process known as dewatering.

To check the water levels in the ground a large number of piezometers (devices for measuring water levels and pressures) were installed across the entire route. An understanding of the ground water conditions allowed engineers to decide where dewatering would be required to assist the tunnelling works.

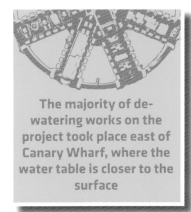

The majority of dewatering works on the project took place east of Canary Wharf, where the water table is closer to the surface

Underground caverns

Six huge caverns were created under London during the project, taking the established sprayed concrete lining technique to new limits. The caverns at Fisher Street, Stepney Green and Whitechapel were created to house crossover points where running tunnels come together to allow trains to move from one track to the other. The largest of these caverns, at Stepney Green, will act as the junction for trains heading east either towards Abbey Wood or Shenfield.

CASE STUDY

STEPNEY GREEN CAVERNS

The Stepney Green caverns are some of the largest mined soft-ground caverns ever constructed in Europe.

Approximately 50 metres long, 17 metres wide and 15 metres high, the caverns were built in advance of the arrival of tunnel boring machines Victoria and Elizabeth, which passed through on their way to Farringdon from the Limmo peninsula. To construct the cavern, the team had to excavate 7,500m³ of material and apply 2,500m³ of shotcrete to the walls.

The ground at Stepney Green was made up of clay, silt and sand units known as the Lambeth Group which had excess levels of water that could cause instability during excavations and make spraying concrete lining difficult. It was necessary to lower the groundwater before excavation could begin. To do this, a method known as depressurisation was used to dewater the area.

The term depressurisation refers to the lowering of groundwater levels. It was done by a combination of drilling boreholes from the surface, around the area of the works and pumping water from the ground. This reduced the groundwater levels significantly, but not quite enough to ensure dry conditions in the tunnel. A further set of wells were installed from within the tunnels and water pumped from the ground as the tunnels advanced.

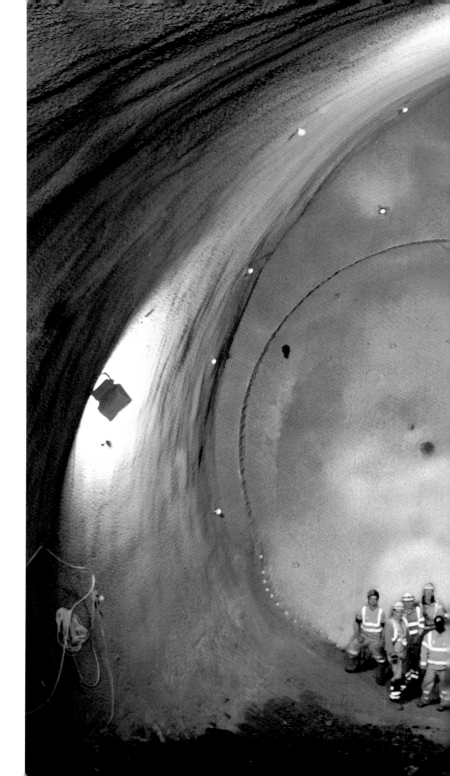

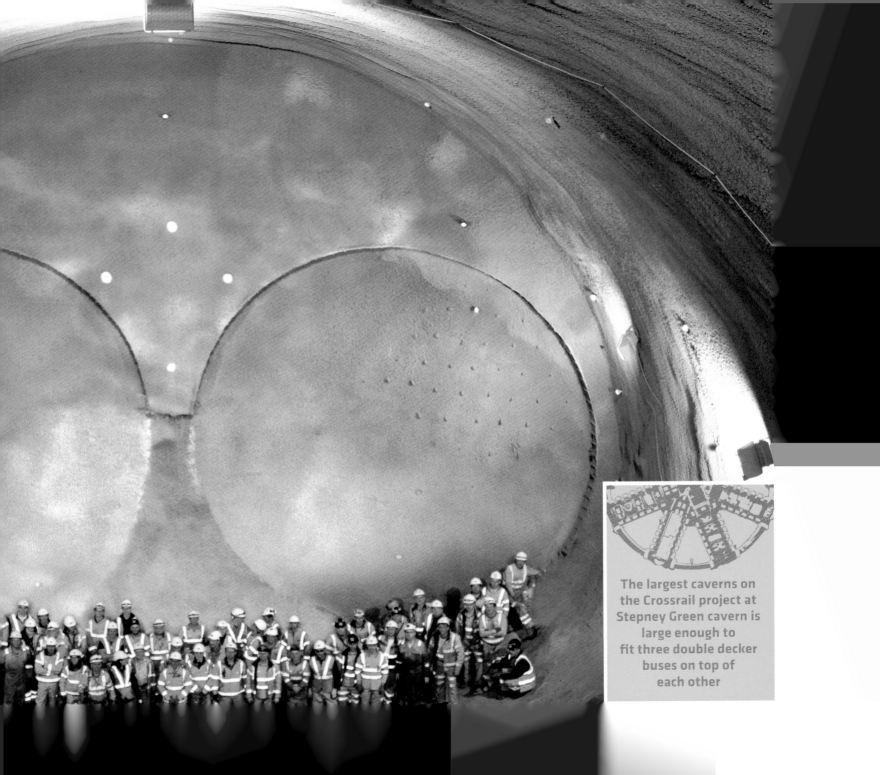

The largest caverns on the Crossrail project at Stepney Green cavern is large enough to fit three double decker buses on top of each other

Fisher Street shaft construction

The 30 metre deep, 15 metre diameter shaft at Fisher Street in central London will not be part of the passenger's normal experience of Crossrail, but it was vital to the construction programme.

During construction, the shaft allowed site access to create two large crossover caverns and also provided access for the construction of running tunnels between Bond Street and Farringdon. When the railway is complete, the shaft will remain as a permanent emergency access route.

The shaft was built by sinking a continuous circle of piles and then excavating within the circumference. Once the team reached the London clay, work progressed with the excavation of one metre sections, stabilised with sprayed concrete lining, until a depth of 30 metres was achieved. At the bottom, cross passages were built to the north and to the south, using the same technique, to connect to the running tunnels.

Once tunnel boring machines Ada and Phyllis had gone past on their way east to Farringdon, the team broke into the running tunnels and constructed the caverns to create 12 metre wide, nine metre high crossover spaces. Much of the work took place below sensitive buildings in confined spaces.

"When you are excavating spaces with sprayed concrete lining you need a continuous supply of concrete. To achieve this in limited space is a challenge. We sank a number of boreholes from the disused Kingsway Tram tunnel into each of our running tunnels and sent the concrete in that way. This was critical to getting a safe and efficient provision of concrete to complete the works."

Andy Alder, Project Manager, Western Tunnels, Bond Street and Tottenham Court Road Station Tunnels

"One of the key things is to have that sense of pride in what you are doing and that is very easy at Farringdon because there are so many things to be proud of. It's brilliant to be a part of this project, it's an amazing opportunity to be at the heart of the Crossrail project and be working on such an amazing station, with great people, changing the lives of Londoners. It doesn't get any better than this."

Nisrine Chartouny
Project Manager, Farringdon

Station platform tunnels

The scale of the Crossrail tunnels will be felt most when passengers walk onto the platforms, a good example being Farringdon station at the heart of the route.

While a London Underground platform is approximately 120 metres long, the Farringdon platforms are approaching 250 metres long and 12 metres in diameter.

The platform spaces in this station were formed around tunnels already constructed by the tunnel boring machines. As each machine drove through the station, it put pre-cast concrete segments in place to support the tunnel it had formed. To enlarge these tunnels into permanent platform spaces, the concrete segments were removed one by one, allowing an excavation in one metre increments, which was spray concrete lined. The lining was tested and another concrete segment removed and so the process advanced.

The working environment at Farringdon was challenging due to prehistoric ground faults and water-bearing pockets of sand. It required tight construction controls and extensive monitoring to mitigate against the risk of ground instability. Five grout shafts, each with a radial array of tubes running up to 80 metres horizontally through the London clay, enabled grout to be injected to precise locations to minimise any movement at ground level.

Exclusion Zone
Strictly No Entry

Tunnelling uphill

An uphill excavator was used for the first time in the UK to build the inclined barrel-shaped tunnel in Whitechapel station. This tunnel will one day house the escalator that will take passengers from the platforms, over 30 metres deep, up to street level.

Due to difficulties accessing the station to dig downwards, an uphill excavator was utilised to allow excavation to start from the platform level and work its way up. This excavator, traditionally used in coal mines, is designed to do two jobs in one. The machine hangs on chains from bolts drilled in the ceiling of the tunnel. It works its way up by excavating using a digger attached at the front, and installing a concrete lining using a spray nozzle, attached to the top of the machine.

The machine is operated by a team of engineers: a driver inside the cabin, an operator who controls the spray concrete nozzle remotely from a purpose-built walkway and two others who monitor safe progress.

The escalator barrel was completed in May 2015, ready for the escalator to be installed as part of the station fit out.

Turning waste into gain

Over seven million tonnes of excavated material were mined during Crossrail's construction. Making good use of this potential waste was an important opportunity.

Some of the excavated material was used to turn marshland, wasteland and landfill sites into useable land, some had to be cleaned and made ready to be reused and some of it was sent to create a large wildlife RSPB reserve at Wallasea Island, in Essex.

In total over 98 per cent of the excavated material was reused to create new agricultural or industrial land, nature reserves and recreational facilities in London and South East.

Nearly 80 percent of material transported to these sites was by rail and water, avoiding significant numbers of lorry journeys on London's roads.

HOW CROSSRAIL HAS REUSED 98% OF EXCAVATED EARTH

The 10 sites that have received the largest tonnage of London earth:

1

CALVERT LANDFILL
Landfill restoration

2

RAINHAM LANDFILL
Landfill restoration

3

FAIRLOP QUARRY
Agricultural and conservation use

4

INGREBOURNE
Golf course

1

□ Bicester

Kidlington

□ Wheatley

Harrow □

□ Uxbridge

Richmond □

Kingston upon Th

Sutton

□ Epso

10 OCKENDON
Landfill restoration engineering prior to creating a wildlife reserve

9 PITSEA LANDFILL
Supporting restoration to RSPB wetland nature reserve

8 WALLASEA ISLAND
RSPB nature reserve and soft coastal defence system

7 KINGSNORTH
Raise land to allow for construction of a commercial park

6 GOSHEMS FARM
Grazing pasture for livestock

5 EAST TILBURY QUARRY
Restoration to RSPB wetland nature reserve

CASE STUDY

WALLASEA ISLAND

Over three million tonnes of excavated earth contributed to the creation of a landmark 1500 acre wildlife habitat at Wallasea Island. A collaborative project between Crossrail and the RSPB, the island will provide a haven for an array of internationally important wildlife.

Wallasea Island will be the largest and most important coastal habitat creation scheme in the UK. It is also one of the UK's most innovative flood defence systems, designed to help combat threats from coastal flooding.

Construction of Wallasea Island began in September 2012 and the habitat received its last shipment of excavated earth from Crossrail in April 2015.

This flagship wetland nature reserve will be twice the size of the City of London

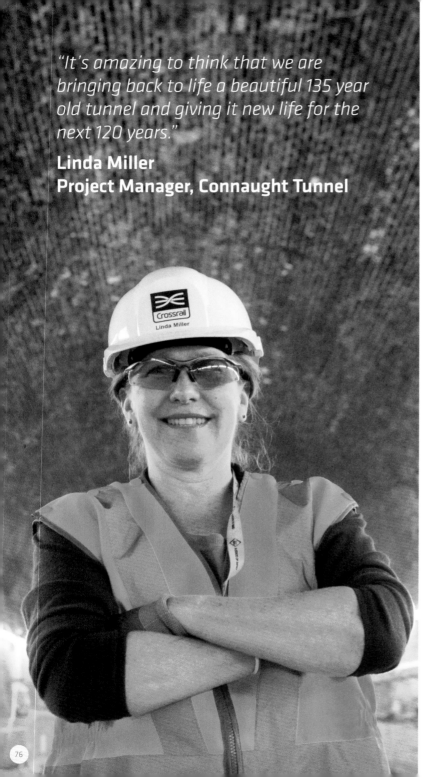

"It's amazing to think that we are bringing back to life a beautiful 135 year old tunnel and giving it new life for the next 120 years."

Linda Miller
Project Manager, Connaught Tunnel

A VICTORIAN REVIVAL

The renovation of Connaught Tunnel was a very different challenge in Crossrail's tunnelling journey. The 550 metre long tunnel ran under the Royal Docks next to ExCeL exhibition centre, close to London City Airport, offering a ready made tunnel to cross the water. Originally built in 1878, to very different specifications to the Crossrail tunnels, it had not been in passenger use since December 2006.

Too small to accommodate the future Crossrail trains and with sections of the tunnel in poor condition, work had to be done to upgrade the structure and remove 135 years of coal and soot from the steam trains that once used it. A cofferdam the size of a football pitch was constructed to drain 13 million litres of water from the docks above the tunnel. A temporary enclosure built within a body of water, the cofferdam allowed the enclosed area to be pumped out, creating a dry work environment for the major works to proceed.

Draining the dock in this way allowed engineers to access the structure from above and deepen, widen and strengthen the original tunnel. Working around the clock for three months, structural improvements were completed, the cofferdam walls removed and the dock reopened in time to allow ships to pass through ahead of a trade exhibition at the London's ExCeL exhibition centre.

The original tunnel served the Royal Docks when they formed the largest enclosed docks in the world, used by large ships from all over the globe

Unearthing London's past

One of the largest and most extensive archaeology investigations in the UK was incorporated into the Crossrail tunnelling programme from the outset. Crossrail's central sites offered an excellent opportunity to gather finds in advance of tunnelling taking place and learn more of the rich history of the capital.

Archaeologists worked across 40 sites and revealed secrets from the prehistoric, Roman and medieval eras and the recent industrial past:

- Liverpool Street: Roman suburb and 16th century Bethlehem burials

- Charterhouse Square: Black Death victims

- Limmo Peninsular, near Canning Town: 19th century Thames Iron Works and Shipbuilding company

- Canary Wharf: 55 million year old amber and mammoth remains

- Paddington Station: Brunel's 19th century Great Western Railway

- Tottenham Court Road: Crosse & Blackwell's 19th century food factory and The Soho Brickworks

- Whitechapel: 19th century Albion Brewery

- Bond Street: The lost River Tyburn

- Stepney Green: Tudor moated manor house

- Pudding Mill Lane: Medieval fish weir

- North Woolwich: Mesolithic hunting camp

- Plumstead: Bronze age landscape

- Royal Oak: Ice age animal remains

LIFE IN SUBURBIA

At Liverpool Street, a suburban Roman road linked Bishopsgate and Moorgate.

Wheel ruts and horse shoes in the road show that it was a well travelled route. Roman domestic artefacts suggest people were living and working here at the east side of the Walbrook river. Archaeologists have found a number of Roman horse and human skulls at this site. These could be finds washed down from the cemeteries further up the Walbrook river, or purposely placed in the river as part of funeral rites.

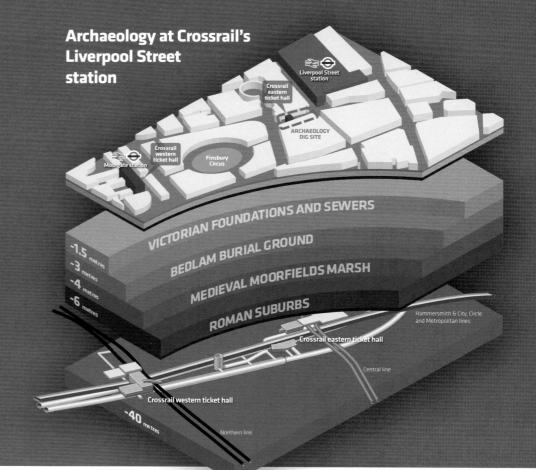

Archaeology at Crossrail's Liverpool Street station

Liverpool Street station

Crossrail eastern ticket hall

ARCHAEOLOGY DIG SITE

Crossrail western ticket hall

Moorgate station

Finsbury Circus

VICTORIAN FOUNDATIONS AND SEWERS

-1.5 metres
-3 metres
-4 metres
-6 metres

BEDLAM BURIAL GROUND

MEDIEVAL MOORFIELDS MARSH

ROMAN SUBURBS

Hammersmith & City, Circle and Metropolitan lines

Crossrail eastern ticket hall

Central line

Crossrail western ticket hall

-40 metres

Northern line

3,000+
skeletons excavated by Crossrail

2,000
years of history beneath Liverpool Street

1
known Roman road running through the site

Archaeology at Crossrail's worksites

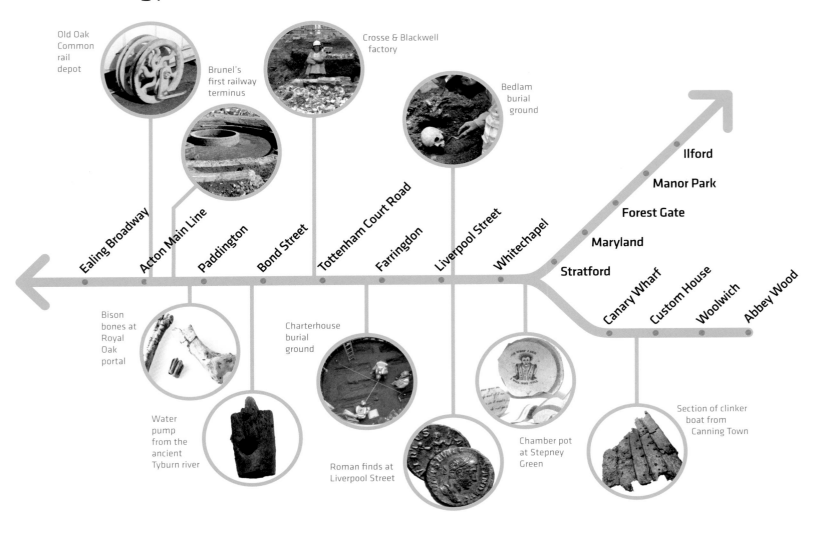

Old Oak Common rail depot

Brunel's first railway terminus

Crosse & Blackwell factory

Bedlam burial ground

Ilford

Manor Park

Forest Gate

Maryland

Stratford

Ealing Broadway

Acton Main Line

Paddington

Bond Street

Tottenham Court Road

Farringdon

Liverpool Street

Whitechapel

Canary Wharf

Custom House

Woolwich

Abbey Wood

Bison bones at Royal Oak portal

Charterhouse burial ground

Water pump from the ancient Tyburn river

Roman finds at Liverpool Street

Chamber pot at Stepney Green

Section of clinker boat from Canning Town

"Excavated finds add to our knowledge of London's past cultures, and will be researched and examined by universities, researchers and archaeologists for years to come."

Jay Carver, Lead Archaeologist

THE FINAL PUSH

"The tunnelling team felt a huge surge of pride when they broke through into Farringdon station. While working on these machines is an everyday experience for these men and women, everyone involved recognised the significance of the final breakthrough and the importance of completing a new tunnel route across London."

Roger Mears, Project Manager
Eastern Running Tunnels

The Big East-West Breakthrough

Elizabeth and Victoria undertook the final tunnelling journey on the Crossrail project. The machines travelled from Limmo peninsula in east London to Farringdon at the heart of the Crossrail route, building over 16 kilometres of tunnel between them.

Vital to the onward progress of the project, these two machines had to arrive at the newly concrete-lined reception chambers at Farringdon's eastern ticket hall on schedule. Tunnellers drove the machines to five millimetre precision, slowing down and reducing the pressure at the face of the machines, to ensure clean breakthroughs into the station.

Elizabeth broke through into the eastbound reception chamber first, followed a few weeks later by Victoria on the westbound route. The final breakthrough on Crossrail took place at 3am on 23 May 2015 in front of a crowd of tunnelling workers who had waited long into the night to witness this historic moment.

The machines finished their work on the project by completing the final rings of the 42 kilometres of Crossrail's new route in Farringdon's eastern ticket hall.

CASE STUDY

BARBICAN CENTRE CITY OF LONDON

Victoria's final journey included tunnelling beneath the Barbican arts centre and residential estate. The programme saw the machines powering under the auditorium during performances by the London Symphony Orchestra.

Special measures including intensive monitoring, specially insulated tracks for the construction railway and speed restrictions for the tunnel boring machines ensured no vibrations or noise interrupted performances.

3 YEARS of underground construction

3.4M tonnes of excavated earth during Crossrail construction

8 custom built tunnel boring machines

200,000+ concrete segments

42 KM of running tunnels

On 4 June 2015 the Prime Minister, David Cameron and Mayor of London, Boris Johnson, visited Crossrail's Farringdon site to celebrate the completion of Crossrail's tunnels. They descended 40 metres below the capital to see the final tunnel boring machine at rest in the station. David Cameron thanked the men and women responsible for building the railway and met some of the tunnellers and apprentices involved in the project.

Celebrations of the big east-west breakthrough continued at Farringdon, at Crossrail's tunnel beneath the Thames and other Crossrail sites, where local residents, stakeholders and members of the public were invited to see the completed Crossrail tunnels for the first time.

The final tunnel boring machines were dismantled and many parts recycled for use on other tunnelling projects around the world. One cutterhead tooth, signed by the Prime Minister, Mayor of London, Secretary of State for Transport and London's Transport Commissioner will be put on public display.

Station construction works at Farringdon before the final breakthrough

The Culture Line

As part of efforts to embed culture within Crossrail, Julie Leonard was appointed the project's official Artist-in-Residence. Julie has created a pictorial diary of Crossrail, capturing many of the personalities, milestones and construction scenes across Europe's largest infrastructure project.

A London-based painter, printmaker and digital artist, Julie used an application on her smartphone to create digital and animated drawings. Working in and around several Crossrail construction sites, she has provided a narrative of the tunnelling project, incorporating stories from the workforce and communities living and working along the route.

Julie's work has helped to capture the story about the people, the spaces and the works going on behind the Crossrail hoardings.

"Just when I thought it was all over, and many of the onlookers had gone, a small door opened behind the cutterhead and an orange clad body popped out waving madly at us from on high. That sight will remain with me. Wow – I was glad I'd loitered after all."

Julie Leonard
Artist-in-Residence

Boring machine Victoria breaks through at Farringdon

3
Voices from the tunnels

HEROIC TUNNELLERS

It took over 10,000 people, working day and night to build the eastbound and westbound tunnels, connecting passageways, station platforms, crossover caverns and other underground spaces.

Their dedication, expertise and hard work has delivered a vital piece of infrastructure that will support the growth of London and the South East and help secure London's place as a vibrant and diverse world city.

For the people on the project, the experience has been far more personal...

"I am very proud of the whole team. There are many, many people who can say 'I built Crossrail's tunnels'"

Andrew Wolstenholme
Chief Executive Officer, Crossrail

**Damian Scanlon
Foreman/Carpenter
DSJV (Limmo, Canning Town)**

"To be part of Crossrail, it's a great achievement... one day the trains will be running through and I'll be sat on a train and I'll be thinking of when I was here..."

Olivia Perkins
Section Engineer
BFK (Bond Street)

"It's an inspiring industry to be a part of because everything you do is really tangible – you can see your output on site. I'll always remember that I was a part of something that thousands, even millions, of people will be using for years and years to come..."

Damien Diver
Fitter/Foreman
DSJV (Limmo, Canning Town)

"My memories include the breakthroughs and the launch of this machine. I built this machine, I ran it, broke through to the Stepney Green cavern and then I dismantled it. It was nice to fulfil the achievement from start to finish with the one machine."

Jay Carver
Lead Archaeologist
Systra (Canary Wharf)

"Crossrail has been a career highlight for me. It's not only the amazing range of different discoveries we've made, but the close collaboration between different teams and the way that everyone has taken positive ownership of the archaeology."

Jules Boyd
Project Controls Manager
Bechtel (Liverpool Street)

*"We have worked incredibly hard to produce all this
under Liverpool Street. When you're busy in the middle of
building on site, its amazing to step back and remember
the full scale of what we're doing."*

Charlotte Ball
Graduate Engineer
BFK (Farringdon)

"I love it here. There's a lot of responsibility. I work on the ticket hall and having a space you can walk through, later on knowing that you built it... that's a great feeling. One of the best things is knowing you're part of building something that's so iconic."

Chris Davis
Managing Director Transportation
Mott MacDonald (Limmo, Canning Town)

"It has been a privilege to be involved with so many talented people working on Crossrail. When it comes into service, the general public will finally be able to see what a great project it is. I can't wait!"

Daniel Ryall
Apprentice Engineer
CSJV (Eleanor Street & Mile End)

"To be one of over 400 apprentices on Crossrail has been a great development opportunity and really advanced my knowledge of tunnelling and engineering."

Mark Whiteman
Site Agent
Morgan Sindall (Pudding Mill Lane)

"The last four years have provided me with a huge range of invaluable civil engineering experience and knowledge. We have faced challenges which could not have been overcome without the dedication of all the teams."

Michael McGrath
Site Manager
HMJV (Thames Tunnels)

"Crossrail is interesting. It's like a gathering together of the clans in terms of the expertise and resources needed to achieve an ultimate goal. It will be absolutely fantastic when it's finished."

Glen Crowland
Programme Controls
Turner & Townsend (Canary Wharf)

"Having previously worked on Tottenham Court Road and Bond Street station upgrades it's great to now be working at Crossrail and see the pieces of the jigsaw joining together."

**Regina Tumblepot
Trainee Engineer
BBMV (Whitechapel)**

*"I've experienced so much
over two years – the fact
that I'm going to make
such a difference to people
across London and make
their lives a lot easier is a
really great feeling."*

Marie Gilmour
Innovation Programme Manager
Transcend (Canary Wharf)

"I've worked with some great people on this job and learned about many aspects of construction. We've been able to progress a real range of innovations so it's been an absolute pleasure to be a part of it."

DSJV (Limmo, Canning Town)

"After this job, I'll be retiring. I've worked on Connaught Tunnel, but the breakthrough was one of the most memorable events of my career."

105

Romeena Haider
Lead Asset Protection Engineer
Arup Atkins (Tottenham Court Road)

"Seeing years of design work coming to fruition is fantastic, especially when the tunnels have been built with little disruption to the city above."

Ryan Donavan
Excavating Miner
BFK (Farringdon)

"In a small space of time, there's been a lot of work done. Farringdon looks totally different from the way it looked a few months ago with the tunnels complete."

**Chris Pateman
Project Manager
Bechtel (Bond Street)**

"It is a fantastic feeling being part of a team that is creating spaces and structures that will form part of London's history."

Rosa Diez
Project Manager
Mott MacDonald (Liverpool Street)

"Two and a half years tunnelling through various challenges has seen the final realisation of the biggest construction project in Europe and the development of a fantastic team - one that I am particularly proud to be part of."

Sam Ahmad
Field Engineer
Systra (Liverpool Street)

"I've been in charge of ensuring the work is being done to specification. After overseeing the sprayed concrete lining works and preparing for the last tunnel boring machines to come through it feels good to see the tunnels complete. We've achieved a lot."

Bandele Odubanjo
Tally Man/Security
DSJV (Limmo, Canning Town)

"We look after the people who go down to the tunnels. If 100 people go down, we make sure 100 people come back up safely."

Leigh Kelly
Administrator
Morgan Sindall (Pudding Mill Lane)

"I enjoy taking part in the progress, successes and challenges that our site has presented us with. Everyone here is enthusiastic about their job and loves educating others with their knowledge."

**Joshua Owens
Apprentice Tunnelling Engineer
CSJV (Eleanor Street & Mile End)**

"I am proud to be involved in the largest infrastructure project in Europe – it's great to have had the opportunity to get a professional qualification plus onsite experience."

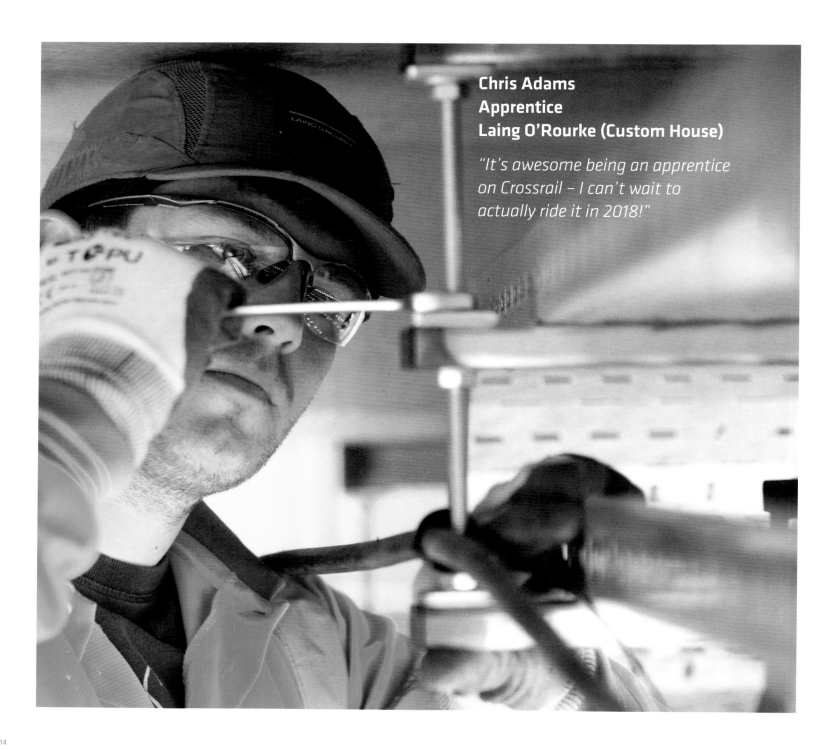

Chris Adams
Apprentice
Laing O'Rourke (Custom House)

"It's awesome being an apprentice on Crossrail – I can't wait to actually ride it in 2018!"

Jeremie Lore
Shift Team Leader
BBMV (Liverpool Street)

"The tunnels are like another world deep beneath London and I look forward to travelling through them one day and being able to say, I helped to build this."

**Sebastian Kohlmeier
Mechanical Engineer/
Service Project Manager
Herrenknecht (Limmo, Canning Town)**

"We don't know nine to five. Our philosophy is: the machines have to run. We only call it a day when everything has run smoothly."

Ailie MacAdam
Delivery Director, Central Section
(2009-2014) Bechtel

"I am immensely proud of what we have achieved as a team on this project. It has been full of great challenges and great people from all backgrounds. But best of all, when we are finished, I know it will make a huge difference to the lives of people living and travelling in and around London."

Dilbag Singh
Traffic Marshall
BFK (Bond Street)

*"My greatest memory will be when
I was working in a tunnel boring
machine down inside the tunnel...it was
incredible."*

Simon Chittenden
Project Field Engineer
CH2M (Thames Tunnels)

"It has been fantastic working on Crossrail for the best part of nine years; seeing the project from scheme design through to the completion of tunnelling. Back in the early days we didn't even know if the project would get built and now we are only a couple of years from having trains running under the centre of London."

Eoin Regan
Site Agent
HMJV (Woolwich)

"I look back with fond memories of what we did. A good team, the amount of work, the excavation, the amount of concrete we brought in, the public communication and focus on safety. No chances have been taken on this job. It has had to be right."

Jorge Zapico & Claude Metz,
Electricians
Herrenknecht (Limmo, Canning Town)

"We've gathered a lot of experience from numerous projects. We are proud that we can support Crossrail with it."

Josh Roy
Section Engineer
BBMV (Whitechapel)

"Working on this project has been a great experience and a worthwhile challenge. Knowing that I've been part of an Infrastructure project which will make a huge difference to London."

Rhaynukaa Soni
Health & Safety Advisor
BFK (Farringdon)

"The sheer size of it... all these works going on in Farringdon are a real testament of the hard work of all the people in these tunnels. It's a very special job to be on. It doesn't matter if you're a girl or a guy... leaving the legacy for generations to come is an amazing thought."

**Graeme Welsh
Tunnel Inspector
DSJV (Stepney Green)**

"I've met a lot of new people coming into the industry and some of the old faces from other big tunnelling jobs. I've been in tunnelling for 30 years. There will be other tunnels to build in the future and hopefully I'll meet some of these people I've worked with again."

Rob Coverdale
Tunnel Fitter
BBMV (Liverpool Street)

"It is surreal down here to begin with. The memory I'll take away is the thought of going to work in London like everyone else but we're here 40 metres under everyone's feet all day. Completing my apprenticeship is a good memory. It's a big project and having your name against that is impressive."

125

Vipul Chandegra
Tunnel Design Engineer
Arup Atkins (Limmo, Canning Town)

"It's been an amazing experience working with some great people to help deliver what will undoubtedly be a first-class railway for London."

Syinyi Phoon
Innovation Coordinator
Transcend (Canary Wharf)

"The best part of working here has been meeting the enthusiastic people working in different roles, listening to their stories and cutting-edge solutions. We all share the pride in delivering this world-class railway."

Dan Bennett
Electrician
Laing O'Rourke (Custom House)

"I'm proud to be a sparks on the job. It's been amazing watching the new station go up at Custom House – what a boost for east London."

Nazia Malik
Project Controls Engineer
Turner & Townsend (Canary Wharf)

"To see history in the making is an extraordinary feeling and knowing that I play a part in it makes me feel proud. It is definitely an experience I will share with my loved ones for many years to come."

2015 marked the end of Crossrail's tunnelling journey. The biggest construction project in a generation has completed a major new asset under the city, but there is plenty more to do to build a railway.

In the coming years the tunnels will be fitted out, new stations will be completed, existing stations will be upgraded and new trains will be manufactured.

The public will get its first real view of the tunnels in 2018 when Crossrail services open through central London, bringing a step change in travel to the capital.

Thank you to our partners

TO EVERYONE INVOLVED

The tunnelling achievement of the Crossrail project has been the result of a huge extended family working with Crossrail to move London forward.

The construction phase supports over 55,000 jobs across the UK and provides over 75,000 business opportunities. Building a family committed to shared values and a single goal has been central to the project's success.

"I would like to say thank you to our extended family for their ambition, their commitment, their skill and their collaboration.

We can all be proud of what we have achieved in delivering these new underground tunnels for London."

Andrew Wolstenholme
Chief Executive Officer, Crossrail

133

ARUP ATKINS

Arup and Atkins, in joint venture, designed the 42km of Crossrail bored tunnels that pass under central London. The team had to plan how to thread the tunnels through the congested subterranean world, weaving them around building foundations, London Underground tunnels and a host of other structures and utilities. Thousands of hours were spent assessing how 17,000 buildings (many listed), railways, major utilities and other infrastructure adjacent to the route may respond to the tunnelling. These assessments combined with monitoring during construction meant the huge expanse of tunnels could be built with minimal disturbance to the city above.

BBMV

Joint venture BBMV consists of Balfour Beatty, BeMo Tunnelling, Morgan Sindall and VINCI Construction. The four leading international engineering companies worked together to deliver station and tunnel infrastructure at Liverpool Street and Whitechapel Stations for Crossrail. Together the four businesses employ more than 200,000 people and have a combined turnover exceeding £40 billion world-wide, £10 billion of which is achieved in the UK.

BAM FERROVIAL KIER (BFK)

BFK is a joint venture of BAM, Ferrovial and Kier comprising three of the world's leading tunnelling, civil engineering and construction companies. As recognised industry leaders in infrastructure projects, they have an established capability in the delivery of complex railway and tunnel projects.

BFK was awarded a number of contracts including the construction of 6.4km twin tunnels Royal Oak Portal -Farringdon, Bond Street and Tottenham Court Road station caverns, ventilation shaft and crossover at Fisher Street, 5 cross passages, east and west ticket hall construction at Farringdon Station plus 1.4km of platform tunnels, cross passages and mechanical, electrical and plumbing works.

BECHTEL

Bechtel is part of the integrated management team on Crossrail. Along with Systra and Halcrow (a CH2M company) Bechtel is employed as the Project Delivery Partner for the central 21km tunnel section and eight new stations from Paddington through Canary Wharf to the southeast and through Pudding Mill Lane to the northeast. Bechtel is also the delivery partner for Network Rail and its extensive Crossrail programme to upgrade the existing rail network.

Bechtel operates through four global business units that specialise in infrastructure; mining and metals; nuclear, security and environmental; and oil, gas, and chemicals. Since its founding in 1898, the company has worked on more than 25,000 projects in 160 countries on all seven continents. Today, 58,000 colleagues with customers, partners and suppliers deliver on diverse projects in nearly 40 countries.

CH2M

CH2M is proud to be part of the team delivering Crossrail for London. As part of Transcend, the programme partner joint venture, CH2M is providing programme management expertise to Crossrail. Working with Bechtel and Systra, CH2M is providing engineering design and project management services for the delivery of Crossrail's central tunnel section.

Employee-owned CH2M is one of the world's leading consulting, design, design-build, operations, and programme management companies serving government, civil, industrial and energy clients. The company employs over 25,000 people worldwide, and over 2,500 people in the UK.

COSTAIN-SKANSKA

Costain–Skanska Joint Venture was responsible for forming the sprayed concrete underground caverns at Mile End Park and Eleanor Street in East London, along with 13 other contracts on Crossrail.

Costain is one of the UK's leading engineering solutions providers, with a unique focus on major customers who are meeting national needs. The company's tunnelling expertise builds on the Channel Tunnel, Jubilee Line and HS1. Skanska is one of the world's leading project development and construction groups. In the UK, the company has delivered iconic structures like the Gherkin as well as major infrastructure projects such as upgrading the M25 motorway.

DRAGADOS SA

Dragados SA are a key part of the construction arm of the world-leading ACS Group which operates in 68 countries and is currently top of the 2014 ENR 250 Global Contractor List. Dragados are very proud to be a key partner in the delivery of this iconic project constructing 22.5km of twin concrete lined running tunnels in the eastern region. This is one of the largest Crossrail projects using four tunnel boring machines to complete the works in 30 months through some of London's most historic and densely populated business areas . The team has taken more than 80% of lorry journeys off the streets of London by making full use of the River Thames to transport materials and have provided job opportunities for 55 apprentices from the local community.

HERRENKNECHT

Using a total of eight Herrenknecht tunnel boring machines Crossrail successfully completed 42km of new running tunnels under London.

Herrenknecht is the leading premium provider worldwide for all-around technical solutions in mechanised tunnelling. Metro, railway, road, utility, pipeline, hydropower, mining and exploration: Pioneering technology from Herrenknecht ensures safe progress when constructing modern infrastructures in all areas.

Joint Venture

HOCHTIEF MURPHY

Hochtief Murphy is an established joint venture with a track record of over 800km of tunnelling excellence and innovative and successful delivery of complex infrastructure projects. Hochtief Murphy Joint Venture's legacy includes Crossrail Thames Tunnel and Channel Tunnel Rail Link Thames Tunnel.

Hochtief is a world leader in infrastructure solutions with a rich heritage in engineering excellence, providing expertise in tunnelling, transportation, energy and civil and structural engineering. Murphy is a leading multi-disciplined engineering and construction company known for providing safe, innovative and sustainable solutions to the most complex infrastructure challenges across the UK and internationally.

LAING O'ROURKE

Laing O'Rourke delivered three of ten new Crossrail stations. At Custom House, manufacturing all structural elements off site through a unique Design for Manufacture and Assembly approach ensured this critical station was the first to be handed over for station fit out. At Liverpool Street and Tottenham Court Road, the complex tunnel, concourse and passage linings were modelled using digital engineering.

With a heritage spanning over 150 years, Laing O'Rourke is an internationally-focused engineering enterprise, operating an integrated business model that includes engineering, construction and asset management services; delivering solutions for some of the world's most prestigious organisations.

MORGAN SINDALL

Morgan Sindall undertook construction works on the Pudding Mill Lane tunnel portal and a new DLR station, and as part of the joint venture BBMV, works on Whitechapel and Liverpool Street Station tunnels and main station works at Whitechapel.

Morgan Sindall is a UK construction, infrastructure and design business. The company works for private and public sector customers on projects and frameworks from £50,000 to over £1 billion. It operates across commercial, defence, education, energy, healthcare, industrial, leisure, retail, transport and water markets. Morgan Sindall is part of Morgan Sindall Group plc, a leading UK construction and regeneration group with revenue over £2 billion operating through five divisions of construction and infrastructure, fit out, affordable housing, urban regeneration and investments.

MOTT MACDONALD

Mott MacDonald worked on eight of the 24 design contracts, including leading-edge tunnelling, station, signalling, power, ventilation and safety systems design, and specifications for rolling stock, materials and workmanship. Innovations for Crossrail includes the construction of one of the largest caverns in London at Stepney Green, use of GIS systems for excavation control and spray concrete lining techniques.

Mott MacDonald is a diverse £1.3bn global management, engineering and development consultancy. As one of the world's largest employee-owned companies with over 16,000 staff, offices in nearly 50 countries, the company works on public and private sector projects in buildings, communications, education, environment, health, industry, international development, mining, oil and gas, power, transport, urban development, water and wastewater.

SISK

Sisk undertakes all aspects of civil engineering works and in joint venture, with Dragados, on Crossrail's eastern running tunnels. The company safely delivered infrastructure design, logistics and enabling works; construction of shafts and cofferdams; pre-cast concrete segment factory operations; the management of utility diversions; and marine transportations of tunnel segments and spoil.

John Sisk & Son, a member of the SISK Group, is an international construction company which places strong emphasis on safety, performance, quality, teamwork and a "hands-on" management approach. Family ownership over five generations has created a strong foundation of integrity, consistency and fair treatment essential for long term client satisfaction.

SYSTRA

Systra was appointed by Crossrail as part of the Project Delivery Partner (PDP) team to manage delivery of the Crossrail Project with Bechtel and Halcrow (a CH2M company).

The company provide expertise in Railway Systems, Operations, Civil and Tunnel Engineering for the 21km of tunnels and eight new stations.

The Systra Group operates globally, a subsidiary of RATP and SNCF, it has 4,700 staff worldwide, providing engineering services, consultancy and transport planning in over 150 countries.

In the UK Systra has circa 200 engineers/consultants across seven offices in the UK and Ireland.

TRANSCEND

Transcend is Crossrail's Programme Partner and, as part of the integrated project team, has provided the highest standards of planning, programme controls and delivery support to the Crossrail project. Transcend is a joint venture between three world class companies: AECOM; CH2M; and the Nichols Group. It also includes two highly valued sub-consultants Turner & Townsend and Unipart Logistics.

TURNER & TOWNSEND

As a key part of Transcend joint venture, Turner & Townsend provide integrated programme and delivery management services to Crossrail.

Turner & Townsend is an independent professional services company specialising in programme, project and cost management and consulting across the property, infrastructure and natural resources sectors. With offices in 36 countries, the company draws on extensive global and industry experience to manage risk and performance during the construction and operation of clients' assets. In the UK, the company has delivered on infrastructure projects in excess of £100 billion, including Heathrow Terminal 2, Crossrail, Edinburgh Tram and Tottenham Court Road station redevelopment.